Key Stage 1 **LEARN**

Reading & Spelling

NAPE
National Association for Primary Education

Contents

AUTHOR: Camilla de la Bédoyère
EDITORIAL: Catherine de la Bédoyère, Quentin de la Bédoyère, John Bolt, Vicky Garrard, Kate Lawson, Sally MacGill, Julia Rolf, Lyndall Willis
DESIGN: Jen Bishop, Dave Jones, Colin Rudderham
ILLUSTRATORS: David Benham, Sarah Wimperis
PRODUCTION: Chris Herbert, Claire Walker
Thanks also to Robert Walster

COMMISSIONING EDITOR: Polly Willis
PUBLISHER AND CREATIVE DIRECTOR: Nick Wells

3 Book Pack ISBN 1-84451-051-4   Book ISBN 1-84451-015-8
6 Book Pack ISBN 1-84451-065-4   Book ISBN 1-84451-073-5
First published in 2003

A copy of the CIP data for this book is available from the British Library upon request.

Created and produced by
FLAME TREE PUBLISHING
Crabtree Hall,
Crabtree Lane,
Fulham, London SW6 6TY
United Kingdom
www.flametreepublishing.com

Flame Tree Publishing is part of The Foundry Creative Media Co. Ltd.

© The Foundry Creative Media Co. Ltd, 2003

Printed in Croatia

Foreword

Sometimes when I am crossing the playground on my way to visit a primary school I pass young children playing at schools. There is always a stern authoritarian little teacher at the front laying down the law to the unruly group of children in the pretend class. This puzzles me a little because the school I am visiting is very far from being like the children's play. Where do they get this Victorian view of what school is like? Perhaps it's handed down from generation to generation through the genes. Certainly they don't get it from their primary school. Teachers today are more often found alongside their pupils, who are learning by actually doing things for themselves, rather than merely listening and obeying instructions.

Busy children, interested and involved in their classroom reflect what we know about how they learn. Of course they learn from teachers but most of all they learn from their experience of life and their life is spent both in and out of school. Indeed, if we compare the impact upon children of even the finest schools and teachers, we find that three or four times as great an impact is made by the reality of children's lives outside the school. That reality has the parent at the all important centre. No adult can have so much impact, for good or ill, as the young child's mother or father.

This book, and others in the series, are founded on the sure belief that the great majority of parents want to help their children grow and learn and that teachers are keen to support them. The days when parents were kept at arm's length from schools are long gone and over the years we have moved well beyond the white line painted on the playground across which no parent must pass without an appointment. Now parents move freely in and out of schools and very often are found in the classrooms backing up the teachers. Both sides of the partnership know how important it is that children should be challenged and stimulated both in and out of school.

Perhaps the most vital part of this book is where parents and children are encouraged to develop activities beyond those offered on the page. The more the children explore and use the ideas and techniques we want them to learn, the more they will make new knowledge of their very own. It's not just getting the right answer, it's growing as a person through gaining skill in action and not only in books. The best way to learn is to live.

I remember reading a story to a group of nine year old boys. The story was about soldiers and of course the boys, bloodthirsty as ever, were hanging on my every word. I came to the word khaki and I asked the group "What colour is khaki?" One boy was quick to answer. "Silver" he said, "It's silver." "Silver? I queried. "Yes," he said with absolute confidence, "silver, my Dad's car key is silver." Now I reckon I'm a pretty good teller of stories to children but when it came down to it, all my dramatic reading of a gripping story gave way immediately to the power of the boy's experience of life. That meant so much more to him, as it does to all children.

JOHN COE
General Secretary
National Association for Primary Education (NAPE).

NAPE was founded 23 years ago with the aim of improving the quality of teaching and learning in primary schools. The association brings together parents and teachers in partnership.

NAPE, Moulton College, Moulton, Northampton, NN3 7RR, Telephone: 01604 647 646 Web: www. nape.org.uk

Reading & Spelling is one of six books in the **Learn Series** for Key Stage One. These books have been devised to help you support your child as they begin Primary School.

This book introduces you and your child to the National Literacy Strategy and it aims to set out the key skills your child will be learning at school. You should go through the book together; your child will need you on hand to guide them through each subject. There are both written and practical activities throughout the book, which will help reinforce the concepts that are covered.

You will also find **Parents Start Here** boxes to give you extra information and guidance.

Before you begin any learning session with the book, ensure your child is relaxed and comfortable:

- They should be sitting with their feet touching the floor and their bottom at the back of their seat.
- Put the book at a slight angle so your child can see their pencil point as they write.
- Encourage a good writing grip and neat presentation of work.
- Give your child access to water; research suggests that children who drink water when they work are able to perform better.

Do not attempt to complete too many pages in one sitting; children have short attention spans and you want the experience to remain pleasurable. Offer your child plenty of praise for the work they accomplish. Reinforce the learning with lots of activities away from the book. The book emphasises the importance of using a variety of reading cues such as phonics, spelling strategies, syntax and context. You can help by making sure your child uses all of these to read.

There is a checklist at the end of the book; you can use this to show your child how they are progressing. You could introduce a reward system too; children benefit enormously from rewards and praise.

Most importantly, the time you spend together with this book should be enjoyable for both of you.

Top Tip!
Go through this page as often as you like until your child understands it fully.

Parents Start Here...

Making letter shapes in dough, sand or shaving foam helps your child to learn their letter formation, sounds and names.

Making Simple Words

There are 26 letters in the alphabet. Here they are:

a b c d e f g h i j k l m n o p q r s t u v w x y z

These letters are vowels: **a e i o u**

The other letters are all consonants, except for y, which sometimes sounds like a vowel and sometimes sounds like a consonant.

Every word we read or write has at least one vowel (or y) in it.

Put the missing vowels into these words:

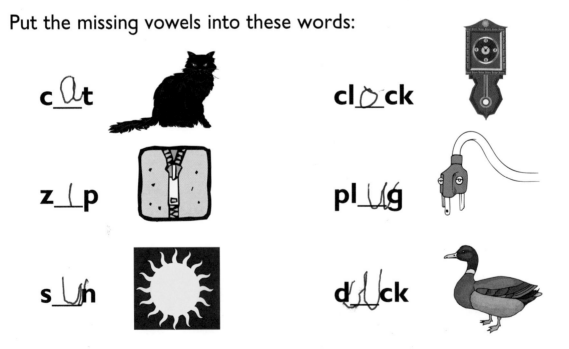

c_a_t

cl_o_ck

z_i_p

pl_u_g

s_u_n

d_u_ck

These words need a letter y, which will make the sound of i when you say its name. Write the y and read the word.

sk_   st_y   cr_y   m_y

These words need a letter y, but this time the y will make the sound of e when you say its name. Write the y and read the word.

happ_y   luck_y   sogg_y   napp_y

Home Learn

a) (Circle) the vowels:

 bl**a**ck   m**ou**se   r**ea**ch   h**o**pp**i**ng   f**i**sh

b) (Circle) the consonants:

large   extra   cake   bits   running

 ## Activity

Make some letter shapes out of salt dough or Plasticine. Make some words using the letters.

Check Your Progress!
Making Simple Words   24/24 ✓ well done

Turn to page 48 and put a tick next to what you have just learned.

Top Tip!
Don't worry if your child does not understand straightaway – children learn at different speeds.

Parents Start Here...

Letters and groups of letters that give us sounds are called phonemes and they are used in schools to help children build words. We will be covering plenty more phonemes in this book.

Word Building 1

We can make more words using the sounds of letters. We add the sounds together, until we can read the word. Sometimes groups of letters can give us a sound.

s + l + i + p ⟶ **slip**

h + e + l + p ⟶ **help**

r + am ⟶ **ram**

h + at ⟶ **hat**

Read out the letter sounds to make a word. When you know what the word is you can write it in the space.

p + i + g ⟶ _____

p + a + ck ⟶ _____

sp + i + ll ⟶ _____

tr + i + p ⟶ _____

sn + a + p ⟶ _____

b + a + t ⟶ _____

Home Learn

1. Write down 5 words that end with the sound –ig. The first one has been done for you:

a) pig   b)_____   c)_____   d)_____   e)_____

2. Write down 5 words that end in the sound –at. The first one has been done for you.

a) bat   b)_____   c)_____   d)_____   e)_____

Activity

Ask a grown-up to help you with this activity. Using coloured card and scissors cut out some letter and sound cards. Make each card about the size of a playing card and write a letter of the alphabet on each one. Add sounds or groups of letters as you learn them. You could use different colours for vowels and consonants. Use your cards to make words and learn spellings.

Check Your Progress!
Word Building 1
Turn to page 48 and put a tick next to what you have just learned.

Parents Start Here...

Top Tip!
If your child loses concentration here, let them take a break.

You can help your child to spot adjectives by asking questions like 'what kind of clock was it?'.

Words With A Job To Do

A **noun** is the name of a thing or a person.

These are all nouns:

clock   saucepan    hen

Some nouns are always written with capital letters at the beginning. They are the names of actual people, things or places.

> **Stan loves eating Solar chocolate bars in Solihull.**

Put an in front of a noun that starts with a vowel.

> **an apple**

Put a in front of a noun that starts with a consonant.

> **a banana**

Circle the nouns in the sentence:

> **The fox ran away from the dogs.**

A **verb** is a word that tells us what someone, or something, is doing.

> **The comet shot through the night sky.**

Verbs may need two words:

> **The sparrow was pecking at the ground.**

Circle the verbs in the sentences:

Trees fell in the Great Storm of 1987.

He was cycling down the road.

Adjectives are words that describe a noun:

big   **clean**   **pink**

Write two more adjectives:

_____ and _____

Home Learn

Circle the adjectives:

a) The brown horse went home.

b) Billy loves his brave dog.

c) The big clock fell on the polished floor.

d) Ali likes the clean carpet.

Activity

Can you find more adjectives in your reading book?

Check Your Progress!
Words With A Job To Do

Turn to page 48 and put a tick next to what you have just learned.

Activities

1. Fred the fisherman has caught some alphabet fish. Circle the fish that have vowels.

2. Dom is carrying noun balloons, Susie is carrying verb balloons and Chan is carrying adjective balloons. All the strings have got tangled up. Trace the strings with your pencil to check everyone is still holding the right balloons.

3. Granny is sorting out some of her favourite words. She is putting the words that need 'a' in front of them in Basket A and the words that need 'an' put in front of them are going in to Basket B.

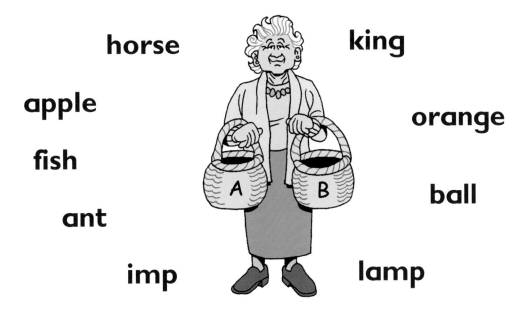

horse

king

apple

orange

fish

ant

ball

imp

lamp

Draw a line from each word to the proper basket.

4. Draw a ring around the nouns that should be written with a capital letter:

peter	christmas	shirt
phone	jam	england
paper	monday	pink

Write them out properly:

_____

_____

Top Tip! Remember to give your child lots of praise – they'll work so much better.

Parents Start Here...

Encourage your child to look after all the books they use.

Let's Look At A Book

Take out your favourite book and have a good look at it.

Answer these questions:

What is it called? _____

Is it a story book?   yes ☐ no ☐

Is it a book just about facts?   yes ☐ no ☐

Does it have a page at the beginning which

lists the stories or the chapters in the book?   yes ☐ no ☐

Who wrote the book?   _____

Who drew the pictures?   _____

Does your book have photographs in it?   yes ☐ no ☐

Why do you think other people should read **your** favourite book?

_____

_____

Books Are Important

You can keep your favourite books forever if you look after them properly. If you borrow books from the library or school you should take good care of them, so other children can enjoy them too.

- **Make sure your hands are clean.**

- Never bend a book back so that it cracks. Before long it will fall to pieces, or pages will come out.

- **Never write in a book, except a book like this one which is meant to be written in. But you can ask a grown-up if you can write your name in the front of your own books.**

- Never turn down the corner of a page to remember where you are. Use a slip of paper as a book mark, or make your own book mark.

- **If you need to carry a book in your school bag check you have put it in carefully and that it will not get covered in bits of your lunch!**

- If you lend a book to a friend, keep a note of who has got it. Then you can ask for it back later.

- **If you borrow a book from a friend or a library, look after it with great care. Remember to return it promptly.**

- Never leave a book on the floor, where it can be kicked or someone can trip over it. Put it back in a shelf or on a table until you need it next.

Activity

Make a bookmark for yourself, or as a present for someone else.

Check Your Progress!
Let's Look At A Book
Turn to page 48 and put a tick next to what you have just learned.

Top Tip!
If your child struggles with anything, don't worry – let them go at their own pace.

Parents Start Here...

Learning to spell by the look/cover/write/check method is very popular in schools, but it only works if you train your child to really look at the word. Encourage them to search for any familiar letter patterns or sounds and keep an eye out for doubles etc.

Days And Months

You need to learn how to read and spell the days of the week.

Step One	Step Two	Step Three
Look at the word and learn it. Cover this list with paper.	Write the word down and check if it is correct. Cover.	Write the word again. Say the word.
Sunday	_____	_____
Monday	_____	_____
Tuesday	_____	_____
Wednesday	_____	_____
Thursday	_____	_____
Friday	_____	_____
Saturday	_____	_____

Here is a very old rhyme which you can learn by heart:

Monday's child is fair of face,
Tuesday's child is full of grace,
Wednesday's child is full of woe,
Thursday's child has far to go,
Friday's child is loving and giving,
Saturday's child works hard for a living,
And the child that is born on the Sabbath day
Is bonny and blithe and good and gay.

You need to learn how to read and spell the months of the year.

Use the look/cover/write/check method to help you, as you did for the days of the week.

January   _____   _____
February   _____   _____
March   _____   _____
April   _____   _____
May   _____   _____
June   _____   _____
July   _____   _____
August   _____   _____
September   _____   _____
October   _____   _____
November   _____   _____
December   _____   _____

Home Learn

1. On what day of the week were you born?_____

2. In which month were you born?_____

Activity

Here is a rhyme to learn. It will remind you of the number of days in each month:

30 days hath September,
April, June and November,
All the rest have 31, except February alone,
Which has 28 days clear
And 29 in each leap year.

Check Your Progress!
Days And Months

Turn to page 48 and put a tick next to what you have just learned.

Top Tip!
Bring what your child learns into everyday life – they'll remember it even better.

Parents Start Here...

If your child has been able to chop compound words up quite easily you could show them how to chop other types of word. September, for example, can be chopped to make Sep-tem-ber. Chopping is an essential skill for reading.

Other examples you could try include: vinegar, silver, shampoo etc.

Compound Words

Compound words are made up of two words joined together.

Chopping up compound words can make it easier to spell and read them.

sun + shine ⟶ sunshine

Join these two words together to make a new word:

some + body ➡		suit + case ➡	
house + fly ➡		dust + bin ➡	
no + body ➡		foot + ball ➡	
bed + room ➡		play + time ➡	
ever + green ➡		goal + keeper ➡	
face + cloth ➡		motor + way ➡	
paper + clip ➡			

Home Learn

Chop up these compound words to make two smaller words.

anything

basketball

playground

windmill

hairbrush

grandfather

tablecloth

sandcastle

seaside

milkshake

hamburger

Activity

Think of words you can add on to the end of these words to make new ones:

horse _____ **, book** _____ **,drain** _____

Check Your Progress!
Compound Words
Turn to page 48 and put a tick next to what you have just learned.

Top Tip!
Learning is fun, so if your child is tired, let them come back to this when they are fresh.

Parents Start Here...

Help your child to make some more sound cards and write these new sounds on to them. Experiment together to explore which new words you can make.

Word Building 2

We know that we can add sounds together to make words.

d + o + g ⟶ dog

Some groups of letters always make the same sound:

ch makes the sound like the beginning of **cheese**

sh makes the sound like the beginning of **ship**

th makes the sound like the beginning of **thumb**

st makes the sound like the beginning of **stamp**

st also makes the sound like the end of **toast**

First Class

Write the new words:

ch + i + p	⟶	_____
ch + i + n	⟶	_____
sh + o + t	⟶	_____
sh + i + n	⟶	_____
th + i + n	⟶	_____
st + a + b	⟶	_____

ck makes a sound like the end of clock

Lots of words end in –**ck**.

t + i + ck

t + o + ck

l + i + ck

l + o + ck

Home Learn

Read these words using their sounds:

chicken ⟶ ch – i – ck – en

thick ⟶ th – i – ck

shock ⟶ sh – o – ck

shack ⟶ sh – a – ck

stick ⟶ st – i – ck

Activity

Add these sounds to your collection of letters and sounds. See if you can make some new words.

Check Your Progress!
Word Building 2
Turn to page 48 and put a tick next to what you have just learned.

Top Tip! Remember to give your child lots of praise – they'll work so much better.

Parents Start Here...

Learning spelling rules (which is what your child is doing here) helps them to read and will enable them to grasp more complicated spellings later on.

Word Building Using Sounds 1

Here are some more sounds for you to learn:

These two groups of letters make the same sound. They make the same sound as the letter **o** when you say its name.

oa **ow**

coat **window**

Write these words and then say them:

b + oa + t ➡ _____

f + l + oa + t ➡ _____

st + oa + t ➡ _____

r + oa + st ➡ _____

These two groups of letters make the same sound.

oy **oi**

toy **soil**

oy usually comes at the end of a word.

oi usually comes in the middle of a word.

20

Write the correct letters into these words. Remember that oy usually comes at the end of a word and oi comes in the middle of a word.

b_____l   b_____

enj_____   sp_____l

c_____n   ann_____

Use some of these words to finish these sentences:

a) I have a ten pence _____ .

b) Mum put the pan on to _____ .

c) I like to _____ my little brother.

Home Learn

Complete the sentences:

a) I like to r_____ my b_____t on the river.

b) The cork fl_____ts in my bathwater.

c) I enj_____ watching plants gr_____.

d) Jenny likes to sp_____l my games.

Activity

Make some more cards for your collection of sounds and add these four sounds.

Check Your Progress!
Word Building Using Sounds 1
Turn to page 48 and put a tick next to what you have just learned.

21

Parents Start Here...

When your child struggles with a particular word, write it out on a big piece of card and put it somewhere your child will see it daily. Ask them to write the word by moving their fingers in the air.

Word Building Using Sounds 2

Here are some more sounds for you to learn:

These two groups of letters make the same sound. They make the same sound as the letter e when you say its name. This sound is called the long e sound.

ea **ee**
beads **seeds**

Write these words and then say them:

b + ea + t _____

f + l + ee + t _____

sh + ee + t _____

b + ea + st _____

These two groups of letters make the same sound. They make the same sound as the letter a when you say its name.

ay  **ai**
hay **snail**

ay usually comes at the end of a word.　　ai usually comes in the middle of a word.

Write the correct letters into these words. Remember that *ay* usually comes at the end of a word and *ai* comes in the middle of a word.

st_____   r_____n

pl_____   Sp_____n

tr_____n   Mond_____

Use some of these words to finish these sentences:

a) My brother has a _____ set.

b) The day before Tuesday is _____ .

c) I prefer the sun to the _____ .

Home Learn

1. Look at these ea and ee words and write them under the correct picture:

read   **sheep**   **tree**   **bean**

_____   _____   _____   _____

 Activity

Make some more cards for your collection of sounds and add these four sounds.

Check Your Progress!
Word Building Using Sounds 2
Turn to page 48 and put a tick next to what you have just learned.

Activities

1. Jason wants to read a book about spiders. Put a tick next to the book Jason should choose.

A = Miss Meek's Mysteries

B = A Guide To Creepy Crawlies

C = The Lost Sheep

D = My Love Lives Forever

E = The Story Of King Bob

2. Write the day and month of your birthday:

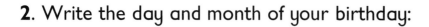

     day   **month**

3. Gerry was in a bad mood and she tore up her word cards. Now she regrets her silliness and wants to stick them back together. Can you help her? One has been done for you.

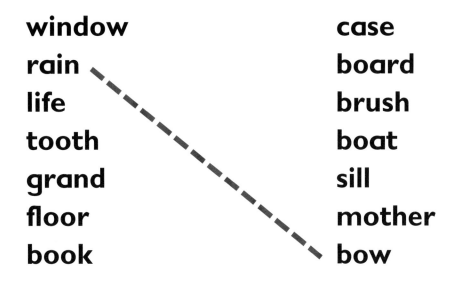

window   case
rain   board
life   brush
tooth   boat
grand   sill
floor   mother
book   bow

4. Morris the Mouse loves adjectives but he can't find any. Help Morris by drawing circles around the adjectives in these sentences:

a) The red bus zoomed down the street.

b) Martians are not green but they are ugly.

c) The nastiest creature I ever met was a crocodile.

d) People say the sky is blue, but I think it is mostly grey.

e) When the waves hit the sand they make a loud noise.

f) My favourite television programme is Storytime.

Top Tip! If your child loses concentration here, let them take a break.

Parents Start Here...

If your child is a natural speller and can spell the numbers here, extend the second exercise to twenty.

Colours And Numbers

You need to learn how to read and spell these colours.

Step One	Step Two	Step Three
Look at the word and learn it. Cover this list with paper.	Write the word down and check if it is correct. Cover.	Write the word again. Say the word.

blue _____ _____

red _____ _____

yellow _____ _____

green _____ _____

orange _____ _____

pink _____ _____

purple _____ _____

You also need to learn how to read and spell these numbers:

Use the look/cover/write/check method to help you, as you did for the colours.

zero _____ _____

one _____ _____

two _____ _____

three _____ _____

four _____ _____

five _____ _____

six _____ _____

seven _____ _____

eight _____ _____

nine _____ _____

ten _____ _____

hundred _____ _____

thousand _____ _____

Home Learn

Complete these sentences using whichever colour or number words you like:

a) My socks are _____.

b) There are _____ cars parked outside.

c) I have _____ sisters and _____ brothers.

d) My front door is _____.

TRY THIS

Activity

Practise writing numbers in words. If you write a number below ten in a story, you should write it in words.

Check Your Progress!
Colours And Numbers
Turn to page 48 and put a tick next to what you have just learned.

Parents Start Here...

Top Tip! Go through this page as often as you like until your child understands it fully.

Help your child to discover the rhythm of the poem by tapping the table or clapping your hands.

Let's Look At A Poem

Read this poem, with a grown-up's help.

A Lifetime

When I was a baby, blond and new,
Everyone asked what I would do.

When I grew up, with mousy hair,
No-one noticed that I was there.

Now that I'm grey, bent like a bow,
What did I do? Does anyone know?

Read it again, but this time think about what the poem is telling you.

Put a tick ☐ next to the correct sentences:

The poem is about a little boy and his baby brother. ☐

The poem is about an old person, remembering. ☐

The person in the poem has a mouse. ☐

The person in the poem had dull-coloured hair. ☐

The person in the poem is happy. ☐

The person in the poem is sad. ☐

The person in the poem has a bent back. ☐

The person in the poem has a bow and arrow. ☐

Home Learn

The poem has a title. Write the title here.

_____

The poem is written in verses, which are separated by spaces. How many verses does this poem have?

_____

Poetry doesn't always have to rhyme, but this one does. Rhymes are words that sound the same.

Do you like rhyming poetry? Yes ☐ No ☐

Why? _____

Find two words which rhyme and write them here.

_____   _____

TRY THIS

Activity

Look at some poetry books. Draw a picture to go with your favourite poem.

Check Your Progress! ☐
Let's Look At A Poem
Turn to page 48 and put a tick next to what you have just learned.

29

Top Tip!
If your child struggles with anything, don't worry – let them go at their own pace.

Parents Start Here...

You will notice that other word blends (phonemes) are being gradually introduced e.g –er, fl– , etc. Your child will probably be reading these naturally once they know to put two sounds together. If not, spend a little time practising them together.

More Sounds 1

Here are some more sounds for you to learn:

These two groups of letters make the same sound. This sound is called the long o sound.

oo
food

ew
screw

Write these words and then say them:

b + oo + t ⟶ _____

f + l + ew ⟶ _____

sh + oo + t ⟶ _____

b + r + ew ⟶ _____

These two groups of letters make the same sound. They make the sound you make if you hurt yourself!

ow
cow

ou
flour

FLOUR

ow!

Write these words and then say them:

t + **ow** + **er** ⟶ _____

fl + **ow** + **er** ⟶ _____

sh + **ou** + **t** ⟶ _____

s + **ou** + **nd** ⟶ _____

Home Learn

Write the words into these sentences:

powder   new   sound   shower   now   trousers

a) Come here, right _____!

b) I prefer a _____ to a bath.

c) I love the _____ of breaking glass.

d) She needed some _____ shirts.

e) She has got lots of old _____.

f) He uses the blue washing _____.

Activity

Have a bubble bath and practise writing your name in the foam.

Check Your Progress!
More Sounds 1
Turn to page 48 and put a tick next to what you have just learned.

Parents Start Here...

Continue to develop your child's writing skills by encouraging play with paints, chalks and pencils.

Magic e

Some words have this letter pattern:

vowel – consonant – e

this is the magic ➞ **e**

The magic e makes the vowel say its name.

The magic e does not make any sound itself.

The magic e does not have to be at the end of a word to work its magic.

Read these words out loud and listen to how the magic e makes the letter a say its name:

hat ➞ hate

cap ➞ cape

pal ➞ pale

tap ➞ tape

Read these words and write the new words made by the magic e. The first one has been done for you.

win ➞ wine

din ➞ _____

pin ⟶ _____

dim ⟶ _____

tim ⟶ _____

hop ⟶ _____

not ⟶ _____

Now you know how a magic e works you can read these words:

like   bike   joke   broke   smoke   brake   make

Home Learn

Draw rings around the words that use the magic e:

shake   feel   (take)   knocked   strike

eating   yellow   help   hole   kite   window   name

roller   Mike   time   slide   key   paper

Activity

Sharpen all of your pencils and keep them upside down in a mug (a clean baked-bean tin also works very well). If you keep your pencils sharp you will be able to produce neat writing.

Check Your Progress!

Magic e ☐

Turn to page 48 and put a tick next to what you have just learned.

Top Tip!
Don't worry if your child does not understand straightaway – children learn at different speeds.

Parents Start Here...

Your child has learnt about a lot of sounds and how they are made. Encourage them to think about rhyming words. They may even be able to predict some of the spellings of unknown rhymes.

More Sounds 2

Here is another sound for you to learn:

This group of letters makes a sound like the letter e saying its name.

ie

thief

Write these words and then say them:

ch + **ie** + **f** ⟶ _____

br + **ie** + **f** ⟶ _____

f + **ie** + **ld** ⟶ _____

This group of letters make a sound that is like the sound you make when you see a very cute kitten.

ar

car

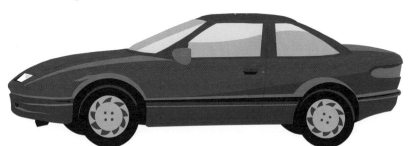

ahhh

Write these words and then say them:

c + ar + t ⟶ _____

p + ar + k ⟶ _____

B + ar + t ⟶ _____

ar + t ⟶ _____

sh + ar + p ⟶ _____

Home Learn

Complete these sentences. Use the word given to you.

stars party field believe harp

a) The farmer put the goat in to the _____.

b) The moon and the _____ were bright.

c) I didn't want her to come to my _____.

d) The angel was playing a _____.

e) I don't _____ a word she says.

Activity

Think of some words that rhyme with park and part.

Check Your Progress!
More Sounds 2

Turn to page 48 and put a tick next to what you have just learned.

The Gingerbread Boy

Read this story out loud:

1 Once upon a time there was a woman who had three very hungry sons. As a special treat she decided to make some gingerbread. There was enough left over to make a gingerbread boy.

2 When the gingerbread was cooked the woman opened the oven. To her surprise, the gingerbread boy got up and ran out of the kitchen. "Where are you going?" she shouted. "I want to eat you!"

3 The gingerbread boy ran out of the cottage, saying "You can't catch me, I'm a gingerbread boy." And he ran out through the farm. The woman's husband and sons joined the chase. They all shouted "where are you going? We want to eat you!"

4 On the gingerbread boy ran, past the chickens, the pigs and the goats. "Where are you going?" shouted the animals. "We want to eat you!" "You can't catch me, I'm a gingerbread boy" laughed the gingerbread boy, as he ran towards the river.

5 When the gingerbread boy got to the river he realised he would not be able to get across. A kind fox stood nearby. "I can help you get across the river" said the kind fox. "Just leap on my head, and I will carry you over."

6 That silly gingerbread boy did what the fox told him. He jumped on to the fox's head. "Just a bit higher," said the fox "then you won't get wet." The gingerbread boy climbed onto the fox's nose just as his mouth went SNAP! The fox gobbled the gingerbread boy all up. Yum!

Put these pictures in to the right order, so they tell the story of the gingerbread boy. Put 1 in the corner of the first picture, 2 in the corner of the second picture, etc.

Check Your Progress!
The Gingerbread Boy
Turn to page 48 and put a tick next to what you have just learned.

Top Tip!
Bring what your child learns into everyday life – they'll remember it even better.

Parents Start Here...

Spelling rules are particularly helpful for children who do not find it easy to remember how common words should be spelt. If your child has a Word Book you could suggest they write some of the rules down, so they can check on them when they need to.

Word Endings 1

Some words end in –ing.

They sound like

king   **ring**

These words are nouns because they are the names of things.

We can add –ing to verbs. (Verbs are words that tell us what something is doing or feeling.)

When adding –ing to words that end in the letter e, we must take off the letter e before adding –ing.

shine ⟶ **shining**
come ⟶ **coming**

Complete these:

hope ⟶ _____

race ⟶ _____

When adding –ing to words that end with a vowel then a consonant, we must double the consonant before adding –ing.

shop ➝ **shopping**

run ➝ **running**

Complete these:

step ➝ _____

wrap ➝ _____

When adding –ing to words that have two consonants at the end, we can just add the –ing.

talk ➝ **talking**

park ➝ **parking**

Complete these:

hunt ➝ _____

milk ➝ _____

Home Learn

Turn these verbs into –ing words:

a) tune ➝ _____

b) win ➝ _____

c) walk ➝ _____

d) hum ➝ _____

e) hop ➝ _____

f) smile ➝ _____

Activity

Go back to the beginning of the book and check you've remembered the vowels correctly.

Check Your Progress!

Word Endings 1

Turn to page 48 and put a tick next to what you have just learned.

Parents Start Here...

Using a white board can be a fun way to let your child practise their spellings. Mistakes are easily rubbed out. They are also a useful tool for handwriting practice.

There are exceptions to the –ed rule – but it does apply to lots of these words so it can be helpful.

Word Endings 2

Some words have the sound –ed at the end.

They sound like

bed  **ted**

These words are nouns because they are the names of things.

We can add –ed to verbs. (Verbs are words that tell us what something is doing or feeling.)

When adding –ed to words that end in the letter e, you can just add the –d, because the e is already there.

like ➝ **liked**

stroke ➝ **stroked**

When adding –ed to words that end with a vowel then a consonant, we double the consonant before adding –ed.

Wag ➝ **wagged**

Wrap ➝ **wrapped**

Some words end in the sound s or z.

They sound like mouse.

s or z at the end of a word is always followed by a magic e.

horse   **priz**e

breeze   **gees**e

size

Home Learn

Give these verbs –ed endings

a) love ➡️ _____

b) hop ➡️ _____

c) hope ➡️ _____

d) skip ➡️ _____

e) use ➡️ _____

Activity

See if you can think of any other words that end in the sound s or z and have the magic e. Clue: it has windows and a roof, and people live in it.

Check Your Progress!
Word Endings 2

Turn to page 48 and put a tick next to what you have just learned.

Top Tip! Remember to give your child lots of praise – they'll work so much better.

Parents Start Here...

Here are some prompts you might like to use when discussing this story with your child:

Who was the story about?

What was the weather like?

Who was the bully in the story, Robert or Billy?

Which grown-up did you like best in the story, and why?

How old do you think the children were in the story?

Do you think you would like to meet Lizzie? Why?

Would you like to have Robert as a friend? Why?

Billy's Story

Read this story with a grown-up.

The playground was covered in puddles, and still the rain continued to pour down. Billy scuffed his school shoes along the ground, kicking the water from left to right. Billy's chin was on his chest and a couple of tears trickled down his nose and vanished into the puddles.

Poor Billy. The day had started so well but things were not looking good now. Billy was going to be in big trouble with Mrs Tooner, the Head Teacher at Billy's school. Billy was on his way to see her; that's why he was crying.

It all started at morning play. Lizzie had been mucking about near the big boys, laughing at them when they played football. Lizzie often did things like that, and it always upset the other children. Robert had missed an easy shot so Lizzie let out a big laugh and pointed her finger at Robert. He came thundering over to Lizzie and punched her in the tummy, hard.

Billy knew it was wrong to hit anyone, but especially wrong for a big boy like Robert to punch a little Year One kid like Lizzie. He ran over and pushed Robert away. Next thing he knew, Billy was being grabbed by Mrs Meaner the dinner lady.

"What do you think you are doing, you great big bully Billy Smith?" shouted Mrs Meaner. She was mean by name and mean by nature.

Before Billy could say anything Mrs Meaner had taken out her notebook and was busy scribbling in it.

"You must go to Mrs Tooner's office at lunchtime." Mrs Meaner had said, before marching off.

Lunchtime had come and Billy was making his way across the wet playground to the Head's office. As soon as he got there he had a shock. Lizzie was standing outside the office, waiting for him with Mrs Tooner.

"Lizzie told me what really happened, Billy" said Mrs Tooner, kindly. "You shouldn't have pushed Robert, but I understand why you did. You won't have a punishment. In fact, I am rather proud of you for trying to look after a younger child. Off you go to lunch now, both of you."

Billy walked to the dining hall with Lizzie, and a spring in his step. It was not such a bad day, after all.

Talk about this story with a grown-up.

> ### Check Your Progress!
> ### Billy's Story ☐
> Turn to page 48 and put a tick next to what you have just learned.

Top Tip!
If your child struggles with anything, don't worry – let them go at their own pace.

Parents Start Here...

Show your child all the different ways writing is used to give us information (e.g. food packaging, magazines and newspapers, Internet, recipes and instructions).

Reading Instructions

Here is a recipe for the best toffee sauce in the world.

Ingredients:
100 g brown sugar • 100 g butter • 100 g golden syrup • 100 g black treacle
One big pot of double cream

1. Weigh out all of the ingredients, except for the cream.

2. Put all of the ingredients, except for the cream, into a saucepan.

3. Put the heat on under the saucepan and stir. A wooden spoon is best.

4. Once the butter has melted and all of the ingredients are beginning to bubble, turn the heat down.

5. Do not let the toffee sauce burn.

6. Gradually add the double cream but keep stirring all of the time.

7. When the cream has all been added heat the toffee sauce for one more minute.

8. Let the sauce cool down a little before you pour it onto ice-cream. You can freeze any leftover toffee sauce, or it will keep in the fridge for one week.

Home Learn

Answer these questions about the recipe:

1. What type of spoon should you use? _____

2. How much butter is needed? _____

3. What do you cook the toffee sauce in? _____

4. Which ingredient do you add last of all? _____

5. What could you do with the leftover toffee sauce? _____

Activity

There is one problem with this recipe. **Have you spotted it**?

You need to have a big pot of double cream. **But how big is a big pot**?

When you write instructions make sure they are clear and have all the information the reader needs.

Write some instructions to a grown-up, **explaining how to play your favourite game**.

> **Check Your Progress!**
> **Reading Instructions**
> Turn to page 48 and put a tick next to what you have just learned.

Wordsearch

Find the months in this wordsearch

S	E	P	T	E	M	B	E	R	O
L	J	R	A	S	A	T	N	I	C
J	U	V	P	A	Y	B	O	M	T
A	N	Q	R	Y	H	D	V	P	O
N	E	E	I	Y	N	K	E	K	B
U	W	C	L	J	A	X	M	F	E
A	E	D	E	C	E	M	B	E	R
R	A	U	G	U	S	T	E	C	N
Y	F	E	B	R	U	A	R	Y	I
J	U	L	Y	P	M	A	R	C	H

January	**February**	**March**
April	**May**	**June**
July	**August**	**September**
October	**November**	**December**

Answers

Page 4

cat   clock
zip   plug
sun   duck

Page 5

sky
sty
cry
my
happy
lucky
soggy
nappy

Home Learn

The vowels are:
black
mouse
reach
hopping
fish
The consonants are:
large
extra
cake
bits
running

Page 7

Home Learn

1. pig, fig, dig, big, rig, prig, jig, wig.
2. bat, cat, fat, hat, rat, mat, pat, sat, chat, tat, vat.

Page 8

The nouns are:
The fox ran away from the dogs.

Page 9

The verbs are:
Trees fell in the Great Storm of 1987.
He was cycling down the road.

Home Learn

The adjectives are:
a) The brown horse went home.
b) Billy loves his brave dog.
c) The big clock fell on the polished floor.
d) Ali likes the clean carpet.

Pages 10–11

1. Alphabet fish: A, I, U, E Y
2. Everyone is still holding the right balloons
3. Granny's Basket A has:
   fish horse ball king lamp
   Basket B has:
   apple ant orange imp
4. Capital letters:
Peter, Christmas, England
Monday

Page 16

somebody
suitcase
housefly
dustbin
nobody
football
bedroom
playtime
evergreen
goalkeeper
facecloth
motorway
paperclip

Page 17

Home Learn

any/thing
basket/ball
play/ground
wind/mill
hair/brush
grand/father
table/cloth
sand/castle
sea/side
milk/shake
ham/burger

Page 21

boil
boy
enjoy
spoil
coin
annoy
a) I have a ten pence coin.
b) Mum put the pan on to boil.
c) I like to annoy my little brother.

Page 21

Home Learn

I like to row my boat on the river.
The cork floats in my bathwater.
I enjoy watching plants grow.
Jenny likes to spoil my games.

Page 23

stay
rain
play
Spain
train
Monday

a) My brother has a train set.
b) The day before Tuesday is Monday.
c) I prefer the sun to the rain.

Home Learn

1. read ....

sheep ....

tree ....

bean ....

Pages 24–25

1. B = A Guide To Creepy Crawlies
3. windowsill
   rainbow
   lifeboat
   toothbrush
   grandmother
   floorboard
   bookcase
4. Adjectives:
a) The red bus zoomed down the street.
b) Martians are not green but they are ugly.
c) The nastiest creature I ever met was a crocodile.
d) People say the sky is blue, but I think it is mostly grey.

e) When the waves hit the sand they make a loud noise.
f) My favourite television programme is Storytime.

Pages 28–29

The poem is about an old person, remembering.
The person in the poem had dull-coloured hair.
The person in the poem is sad.
The person in the poem has a bent back.

Home Learn

The title is 'A Lifetime'.
There are three verses.
The rhyming words are: new/do, hair/there, bow/know.

Page 31

Home Learn

a) Come here, right now!
b) I prefer a shower to a bath.
c) I love the sound of breaking glass.
d) She needed some new shirts.
e) She has got lots of old trousers.
f) He uses the blue washing powder.

Page 33

Home Learn

shake
take
strike
hole
kite
name
Mike
time
slide
paper

Page 35

Home Learn

a) The farmer put the goat in to the field.

b) The moon and the stars were bright.
c) I didn't want her to come to my party.
d) The angel was playing a harp.
e) I don't believe a word she says.

Page 36

The picture numbers appear as follows on the page:
4, 6, 5, 2, 3, 1

Pages 38–39

hope = hoping
race = racing
step = stepping
wrap = wrapping
hunt = hunting
milk = milking

Home Learn

a) tune = tuning
b) win = winning
c) walk = walking
d) hum = humming
e) hop = hopping
f) smile = smiling

Page 41

Home Learn

a) love = loved
b) hop = hopped
c) hope = hoped
d) skip = skipped
e) use = used

Page 45

1. A wooden spoon
2. 100 g
3. A saucepan
4. The double cream
5. Keep it in the fridge or the freezer.

Page 46

S	E	P	T	E	M	B	E	R	O
L	J	R	A	S	A	T	N	I	C
J	U	V	P	A	Y	B	O	M	T
A	N	Q	R	Y	H	D	V	P	O
N	E	E	I	Y	N	K	E	K	B
U	W	C	L	J	A	X	M	F	E
A	E	D	E	C	E	M	B	E	R
R	A	U	G	U	S	T	E	C	N
Y	F	E	B	R	U	A	R	Y	I
J	U	L	Y	P	M	A	R	C	H

Check Your Progress!

Making Simple Words .... ☐

Word Building 1 .... ☐

Words With A Job To Do: .... ☐

Let's Look At A Book .... ☐

Days And Months .... ☐

Compound Words .... ☐

Word Building 2 .... ☐

Word Building Using Sounds 1 .... ☐

Word Building Using Sounds 2 .... ☐

Colours And Numbers .... ☐

Let's Look At A Poem .... ☐

More Sounds 1 .... ☐

Magic e .... ☐

More Sounds 2 .... ☐

The Gingerbread Boy .... ☐

Word Endings 1 .... ☐

Word Endings 2 .... ☐

Billy's Story .... ☐

Reading Instructions .... ☐